Introduction

In a field guide of this nature it is not possible to provide keys to all the many thousands of species of animal found in British freshwaters. Even if vertebrates, microscopic animals and rare species were excluded, a guide several times the length of this would be required. Such a guide would have to make use of features that require very detailed examination of specimens. In many cases it would be necessary to make microscopical preparations of specimens or parts of specimens before identification could be completed. Such techniques are usually beyond the scope of sixth-form field investigations.

A number of available guides include only the more common species. The frequent result of this is that students finding a less common species give it the name of the nearest common relative. (For example, all Amphipoda are regarded as *Gammarus pulex* even though *Crangonyx pseudogracilis* is now a very common species in this country.) It is much more important, however, that students should be trained to use correct names than that everything they find should be identified to species. In this guide we have attempted to take identification to a level that can reasonably be achieved by sixth-formers working in the field or in simple laboratories. Generally, high power magnification is not required although a hand-lens is often essential and a stereo-microscope will be found to be useful.

The Introductory Key should enable students to determine which major group (phylum, class or order) a specimen belongs to. Some groups are not taken beyond this level. However, in most cases, a further key is indicated that will enable identification to be taken to family, genus or species, depending on the difficulty of the group.

More advanced students may want to consult specialist keys listed in the Bibliography or in Armitage, Furse and Wright (1979).

How to use the keys

1 The Introductory Key (Key I) is an example of a dichotomous key. It consists of a series of numbered couplets, each couplet being made up of two contrasting statements **a** and **b**. Occasionally there is a third statement **c**. One of the statements should provide a partial description of the animal you wish to identify. Study the statements carefully and decide which most closely describes your specimen.

2 Each statement ends *either* in an arrow pointing to a number *or* to a box containing the name of the group to which the specimen belongs. If the statement ends in an arrow this means 'go on to' the couplet with the indicated number. Find the number on the left-hand side of the page and continue identification until you reach a statement ending in a box. Many of the boxes lead you to another key and indicate the page number on which the key starts. Turn to that key and continue with the identification. In some cases, no further key is provided but further information can be found on the page indicated.

3 Most of the other keys in the book are also dichotomous and should be used in the same way as the Introductory Key. In those few cases where the pattern is different, users should experience no difficulty provided that they follow through the keys in a logical order.

4 When using the keys, particular attention should be given to terms such as 'seldom', 'often' and 'never'. Qualified statements such as 'if the body surface is hard then it is also jointed' need to be read carefully. Size and colour are not always reliable features and should be used with caution. A specimen which is smaller than a stated size range may be a young or poorly nourished individual.

5 Complex terminology has been kept to a minimum but some scientific terms have had to be used. There is no glossary but anatomical terms are explained in words or diagrams where they are first used.

6 Drawings are provided to help you to understand the statements. Avoid the temptation to flick through the keys searching for a diagram that fits your specimen. This will usually lead to incorrect identification.

7 With experience, students may be able to dispense with the use of the Introductory Key. However, it is not advisable to start any key other than at the first couplet.

BLACKWELL
HABITAT FIELD GUIDES
Invertebrate Animals
of Freshwater

Victor Smith

*Senior Lecturer in Environmental Biology,
Nene College, Northampton*

Michael Quigley

*Senior Lecturer in Environmental Biology,
Nene College, Northampton*

Basil Blackwell

Contents

Introductory Key

1 **a** Animals **with a soft body** and **a hard rigid shell.**
Legs absent.

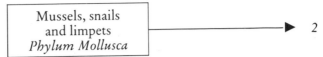

| Mussels, snails and limpets
 Phylum Mollusca |
→ 2

b Animals **without a true shell.** If the body surface is hard then it is also jointed. Legs often present. ———————————————→ 3

2 **a** Shell made up of **two parts** (valves) which hinge together.

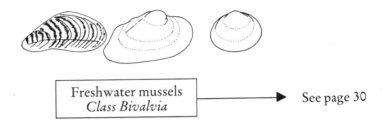

| Freshwater mussels
 Class Bivalvia |
→ See page 30

b Shell consists of **only one part**, coiled or uncoiled.

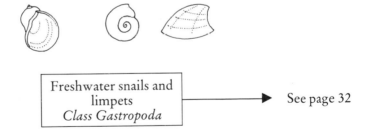

| Freshwater snails and limpets
 Class Gastropoda |
→ See page 32

3 **a** Animals which live **in a case** made of small stones, sand grains, twigs, pieces of leaf or other material. Most move about freely and all have three pairs of jointed legs.

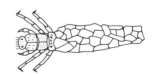

| Cased caddis larvae
 Insect order Trichoptera
 (also some aquatic moth larvae) |

b Animals **without such a case.** (If the animal lives in a tube, it has no jointed legs.) ————————————————————→ 4

4 a Animals **with jointed legs** for walking or swimming.

────────────────▶ 5

b Animals **without legs** or **with unjointed prolegs**.

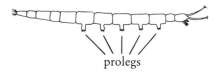

prolegs

────────────────▶ 16

5 a With **three pairs of legs**.

| Adult insects, nymphs and some larvae |
────────────────▶ 6

b With **four pairs of legs**.

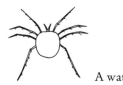

A water mite

| Spiders and mites
Phylum Chelicerata | ────────▶ See page 27

c With **more than four pairs of legs**.

| Crustaceans
Phylum Crustacea | ────────▶ See page 28

6 a Insects with **wings** or **hard wing-cases** (elytra) covering most of the body.

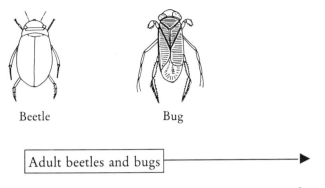

Beetle   Bug

| Adult beetles and bugs | ➤ 7 |

b Insects **without wings** or **wing-cases**.
(Short wing-pads extending to at most the second
and third abdominal segment may be present.)

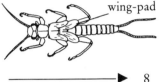

➤ 8

7 a Wing-cases **divided** into distinctly different areas. Head with a piercing
beak or triangular in shape. Antennae **inconspicuous** except in those forms
which live above the water surface.

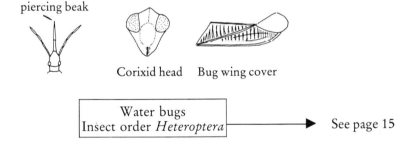

piercing beak   Corixid head   Bug wing cover

| Water bugs
Insect order *Heteroptera* | ➤ See page 15 |

b Wing-cases **not divided** into different areas;
often pitted or grooved. Head with biting
mouthparts and **conspicuous** antennae.

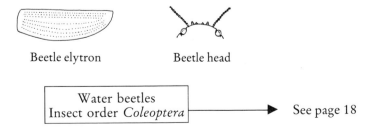

Beetle elytron   Beetle head

| Water beetles
Insect order *Coleoptera* | ➤ See page 18 |

8 **a** Insects **with a piercing beak** or a **triangular head** as in **7a** on page 5.

Immature and wingless bugs

b Insects **without such a piercing beak** and a head **of some other shape.**
━━▶ 9

9 **a** Insect **nymphs with wing-pads** extending to the second or third abdominal segment. ━━━━━━━━━━━━━━━━━━━━━━━━━━━━━━━▶ 10

b Insect **larvae without any trace of wings or wing-pads.** ━━━━━▶ 13

10 **a** Lower lip (labium) modified into **a hinged 'mask'** normally held beneath the head but which can be projected forwards in front of the head. Hind end of nymphs with **three blade-like gill plates** or with **three short processes.**

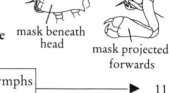

mask beneath head

mask projected forwards

Dragonfly and Damselfly nymphs
Insect order *Odonata* ━━━━━━━━━━━━▶ 11

b Nymphs **without such a mask**; with **two** or **three long slender 'tails'.**
━━▶ 12

11 **a** **Long slender** nymphs with a more or less cylindrical abdomen ending in three gill plates, the longest of which is at least one-third of the length of the abdomen.

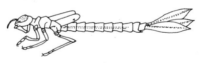

Damselfly nymphs
Suborder Zygoptera

b **Shorter stouter** nymphs with an abdomen somewhat flattened ventrally. External gills absent; the abdomen ends in a number of short spine-like appendages, never as long as one-third of the length of the abdomen.

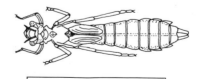

Dragonfly nymphs
Suborder Anisoptera

12 a Nymphs with **three long tapering 'tails'**. Gills on abdomen (may be covered by plates).

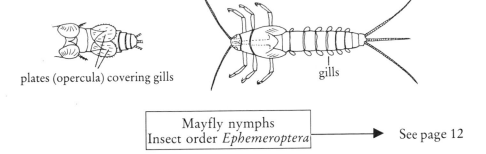

plates (opercula) covering gills   gills

Mayfly nymphs Insect order *Ephemeroptera*

⟶ See page 12

b Nymphs with **only two 'tails'**. Gills, if present, on thorax.

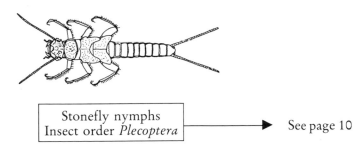

Stonefly nymphs Insect order *Plecoptera*

⟶ See page 10

13 a Larvae **with five pairs of non-jointed prolegs** on the abdomen.

Moth larvae Insect order *Lepidoptera*

b Larvae **without such prolegs.** ⟶ 14

14 a Larvae **with a pair of hooks** on small prolegs at the hind end of the body.

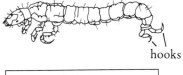

hooks

Caddis larvae Insect order *Trichoptera*

b Larvae **without such hooks.** ⟶ 15

15 a Abdomen **with long jointed filamentous gills** and ending in a single tapering tail. **Large jaws** projecting in front of the head.

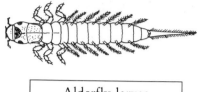

> Alderfly larvae
> Insect order *Megaloptera*

b Larvae **without the above combination of features.**

> Beetle larvae
> Insect order *Coleoptera*

16 a Animals with a **small sucker** around the mouth and a **large sucker** at the posterior end. No hairs or bristles.

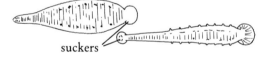

suckers

> Leeches
> *Phylum Annelida*

See page 38

b Animals **without such suckers**. Hairs or bristles often present. 17

17 a Animals with **segmented bodies** (i.e. body divided into similar parts or segments).

18

b Animals with **unsegmented bodies**. 19

18 **a** Body with **less than fifteen segments.** Often with a distinct head capsule and/or unjointed prolegs.

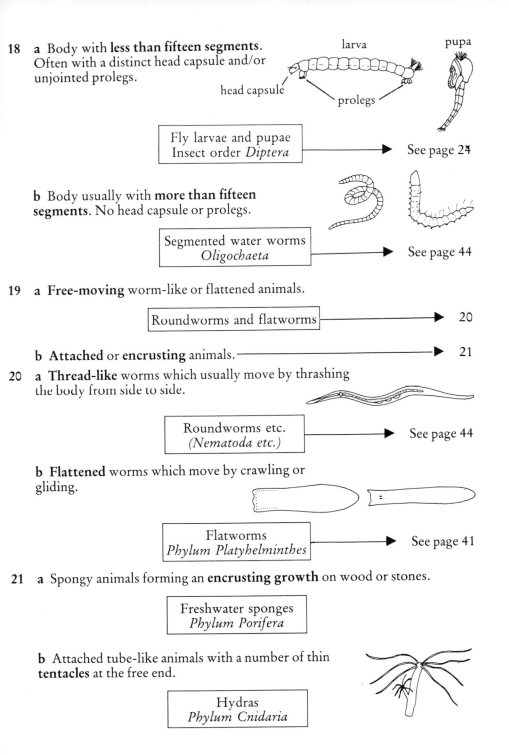

larva   pupa

head capsule

prolegs

> Fly larvae and pupae
> Insect order *Diptera*

→ See page 24

b Body usually with **more than fifteen segments.** No head capsule or prolegs.

> Segmented water worms
> *Oligochaeta*

→ See page 44

19 **a** **Free-moving** worm-like or flattened animals.

> Roundworms and flatworms

→ 20

b **Attached** or **encrusting** animals. ————————————→ 21

20 **a** **Thread-like** worms which usually move by thrashing the body from side to side.

> Roundworms etc.
> *(Nematoda etc.)*

→ See page 44

b **Flattened** worms which move by crawling or gliding.

> Flatworms
> *Phylum Platyhelminthes*

→ See page 41

21 **a** Spongy animals forming an **encrusting growth** on wood or stones.

> Freshwater sponges
> *Phylum Porifera*

b Attached tube-like animals with a number of thin **tentacles** at the free end.

> Hydras
> *Phylum Cnidaria*

Stonefly nymphs (order Plecoptera)

Nymphs preserved in fluid are easier to identify than living or dried specimens. A good quality stereo-microscope is recommended.

1   a   Ventral plate (sternite) of tenth abdominal segment **well developed**. Inner lobes of lower lip (labium) **much smaller** than outer lobes.

tenth abdominal sternite

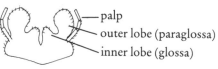

palp
outer lobe (paraglossa)
inner lobe (glossa)

⟶ 2

   b   Sternite of tenth abdominal segment **very narrow**, weakly sclerotised and often covered by ninth sternite so that it may appear to be absent. Inner lobes of labium about the **same size** as the outer lobes.

tenth abdominal sternite

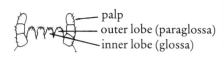

palp
outer lobe (paraglossa)
inner lobe (glossa)

⟶ 4

2   a   **Tufts of gills present** on the sides of the thorax.

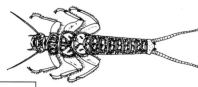

> Family Perlidae
> Genera *Dinocras, Perla*

   b   **No gills** on thorax. ⟶ 3

3   a   Wing-pads as shown in the diagram. Cerci ('tails') less than three-quarters of the length of the abdomen.

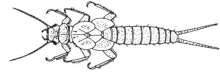

> Family Chloroperlidae
> Genus *Chloroperla*

   b   Posterior wing-pads **set obliquely** to the body. Cerci usually longer.

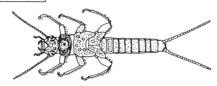

> Family Perlodidae
> Genera *Perlodes, Isoperla, Diura*

4   **a** Second segment of the tarsus as **long or longer** than the first segment.

> Family Taeniopterygidae
> Genera *Taeniopteryx, Brachyptera, Rhabdiopteryx*

  b Second segment of the tarsus **much shorter** than the first segment.

————————————————————————▶ 5

5   **a** **Stout** nymphs with posterior wing-pads set **at an angle** to the body. Hind legs, when stretched back, reach well beyond the tip of the abdomen.

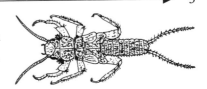

> Family Nemouridae
> Genera *Protonemura, Amphinemura, Nemurella, Nemoura*

  b **Elongate** nymphs with posterior wing-pads **nearly parallel** to the body axis. Hind legs, when stretched back, barely reach end of abdomen.

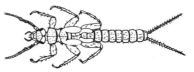

————————————————————————▶ 6

6   **a** Tergites and sternites of fifth to ninth segments fused into **complete rings** (those of first to fourth segments separate). Paraprocts **longer than wide**.

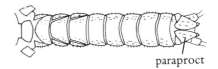

> Family Leuctridae
> Genus *Leuctra*

  b Tergites and sternites of first to ninth segments separated by a membranous fold. Paraprocts **wider than long**.

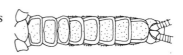

> Family Capniidae
> Genus *Capnia*

Mayfly nymphs (order Ephemeroptera) KEY III

N.B. Only the later nymphal instars with sufficiently developed gills may be identified using this key. The key can be used with either living or preserved specimens but some of the features are more easily seen in living nymphs.

1 a Nymphs with six or seven pairs of **lateral gills** outstretched from the sides of the abdomen and forming a conspicuous feature of the outline of the nymph when viewed from above.

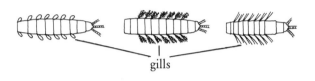

gills

⟶ 2

b Gills not forming a conspicuous feature of the outline of the nymph from above and are either held above the back or covered by large flaps (opercula).

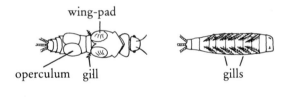

wing-pad

operculum gill   gills

⟶ 6

2 a Nymphs with a **flattened body** and a **broad** head. (Femora also very much flattened.) All or most of the gills consist of a plate and a bunch of filaments.

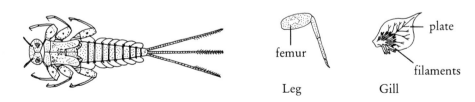

femur

Leg

plate

filaments

Gill

| Family Heptageniidae |
| Genera *Ecdyonurus, Rhithrogena, Heptagenia* |

b Body **more or less rounded** in cross-section and head **less broad**. Gills never consisting of a plate and a bunch of filaments.⟶ 3

3 **a** 'Tails' as long as or **longer** than the body and with only a sparse covering of short hairs.

> Family Leptophlebiidae
> Genera *Habrophlebia, Leptophlebia, Paraleptophlebia*

b 'Tails' **shorter** than the body, usually with a conspicuous fringe of long hairs on both sides of the middle tail and at least one side of the outer tails.

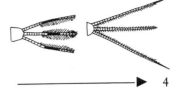

$\longrightarrow$ **4**

4 **a** Gills consisting of **two branches** each thickly fringed with filaments on both sides. Outer 'tails' with fringes on both sides.

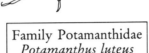

> Family Potamanthidae
> *Potamanthus luteus*

b Gills consisting of **single** or **double plates.** Outer 'tails' with fringes only on inner sides.

Single gill plate   Double gill plate

$\longrightarrow$ **5**

5 **a** Hind corners of last few segments **drawn out into spines** (although they may be small in some cases). All three tails of more or less the same length; each 'tail' with a dark band near its middle but no dark rings between the band and the body.

> Family Siphlonuridae
> Genera *Ameletus, Siphlonurus*

b Hind corners of last few segments **not drawn out into spines.** Either the middle 'tail' is distinctly shorter than the outer ones or the tails have dark rings (and possibly also a dark band).

> Family Baetidae
> Genera *Baetis, Procloen, Cloeon, Centroptilum*

6 **a** Gills **covered by opercula.** (Strictly, each operculum is a modified second gill covering the more posterior gills. The first pair of gills is reduced to inconspicuous tapering filaments.)

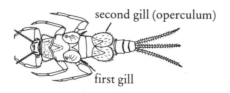

Family Caenidae
Genera *Brachycercus, Caenis*

b Gills held over the back, **not covered by opercula.** ⟶ 7

7 **a** Gills consisting of **two branches** each thickly fringed with filaments on both sides. Each mandible with a long process ('tusk') that projects in front of the head.

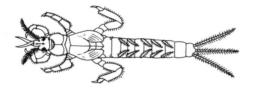

Family Ephemeridae
Genus *Ephemera*

b Gills consisting of **an upper plate** and **two lower arms.** (Apparently four pairs of gills; the fifth is small and usually hidden below the fourth pair.) No 'tusks'.

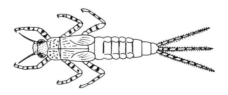

Family Ephemerellidae
Genus *Ephemerella*

Water bugs (order Hemiptera/Heteroptera) KEY IV

1 **a** Bugs that live on the water surface. Antennae conspicuous and longer than the head. ─────────────────────────────────▶ 2

    b Bugs that live beneath the surface. Antennae small and inconspicuous (concealed in pits on the underside of the head). ─────────▶ 7

2 **a** Head **many times longer than broad**. Eyes well in front of the prothorax.

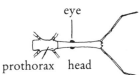

> Family Hydrometridae
> *Hydrometra* species

    b Head **only slightly longer than broad** or **shorter than broad**. Eyes close to the anterior border of the prothorax. ─────────────────────────▶ 3

3 **a** Antennae **with five segments,** the last three distinctly thinner than the first two.

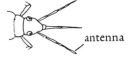

> Family Hebridae
> *Hebrus* species

    b Antennae **with four segments** all more or less of equal thickness. ───▶ 4

4 **a** Prothorax elongated so that the middle legs are inserted **much nearer the hind legs than the front legs**. Hind femora extending well beyond the tip of the abdomen.

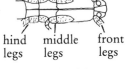

Underside of thorax

> Family Gerridae
> *Gerris* species
> Pond-skaters or Water-striders

    b Middle legs inserted **more or less midway between the front and hind legs**. Hind femora not reaching back beyond the tip of the abdomen. ───────▶ 5

5 **a** All legs inserted near the middle of the body.

> Family Mesoveliidae
> *Mesovelia furcata*

    b Middle and hind legs inserted near to the sides of the body.

> Family Veliidae

─────────────────────▶ 6

6 a Small bugs (1.4–2.5 mm long) with patches of white hairs on the thorax and abdomen. Most of metanotum covered by pronotum or mesonotum.

pronotum

mesonotum

Microvelia species

b Larger bugs (6–8 mm long when fully grown). Small specimens are uniformly black. Metanotum clearly visible in wingless forms.

metanotum

Velia species

7 a Head with a sharp pointed beak which may project forwards in front of the head or may be folded back under the thorax. Scutellum **visible**.

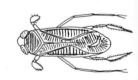

beak

scutellum

beak

⟶ 8

b Head a characteristic shape without such a beak. Scutellum **usually concealed** by the wing-covers.

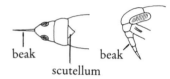

Head

Family Corixidae
Lesser water-boatmen

8 a Crawling bugs **with two long respiratory tubes** at the posterior end of the body (often held together and appearing as one).

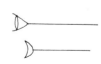

Family Nepidae ⟶ 9

b Swimming bugs **without respiratory tubes.** ⟶ 10

9 **a** Body **long and cylindrical.**

Ranatra linearis The water-stick-insect	

b Body **shorter and flattened.**

Nepa cinerea The water-scorpion	

10 **a** Flat and rather broad bugs which swim **dorsal** side up. Front legs inserted far forward, near the head. ⟶ **11**

b Boat-shaped bugs which swim **ventral** side up. Front legs inserted rather farther back. ⟶ **12**

11 **a** Head **broader than long.** Front legs of characteristic shape. Winged.

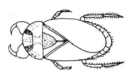

Family Naucoridae
Ilyocoris cimicoides
The saucer bug

b Head **as long as broad**; front legs not as above; usually wingless.

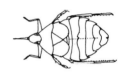

Family Aphelocheiridae
Aphelocheirus aestivalis

12 **a** Very small bugs, 2.5–3 mm long.

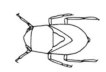

Family Pleidae
Plea leachi

b Large bugs, 13–16 mm long.

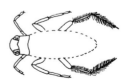

Family Notonectidae
Notonecta species
Water-boatmen or
Backswimmers

Adult water beetles (order Coleoptera)

KEY V

Over 250 species of water beetle are known to occur in Britain. In a work of this nature it is impossible to include a key that would enable identification of even those species most likely to be encountered in freshwater studies. Therefore a key to the families of beetles with aquatic representatives is provided, followed by descriptions of some of the more common or conspicuous members.

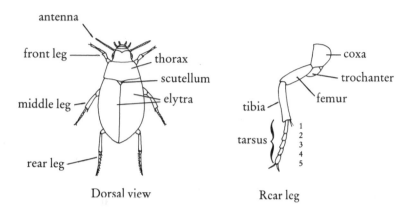

Dorsal view   Rear leg

1   a Middle and hind legs **modified as paddles**, very short, wide and flat. Each compound eye divided into two parts (one ventral and one dorsal). Small shiny black beetles usually found at the water's surface (although capable of submerged swimming).

divided eyes

Rear leg

> Family Gyrinidae
> Whirligig beetles

b Middle and hind legs **not modified** in this way. Eyes not completely divided. ————————————————————————▶ 2

2   a Maxillary palps **as long as, or longer than**, the antennae which are clubbed at the tip. Air is carried in a thin film on the underside of the body.

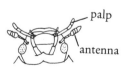

palp

antenna

Head

> Family Hydrophilidae

b Maxillary palps **shorter than** the antennae which are not usually clubbed. Air may be carried but not as a thin film under the body. ————————▶ 3

3 a Hind and middle tarsi **with five segments**, the fourth segment as large or as thick as the third segment.

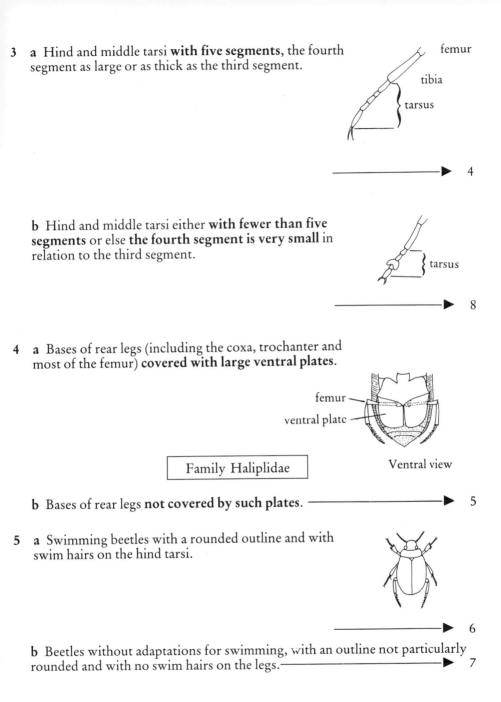

femur

tibia

tarsus

———————▶ 4

b Hind and middle tarsi either **with fewer than five segments** or else **the fourth segment is very small** in relation to the third segment.

tarsus

———————▶ 8

4 a Bases of rear legs (including the coxa, trochanter and most of the femur) **covered with large ventral plates.**

femur

ventral plate

Family Haliplidae

Ventral view

b Bases of rear legs **not covered by such plates.** ———————▶ 5

5 a Swimming beetles with a rounded outline and with swim hairs on the hind tarsi.

———————▶ 6

b Beetles without adaptations for swimming, with an outline not particularly rounded and with no swim hairs on the legs.———————▶ 7

6 a Head **projecting from thorax** with protruding, strongly convex eyes. Hind legs not strongly flattened.

| Family Hygrobiidae |

b Head **deeply sunk into thorax**. Eyes much less convex. Hind legs strongly flattened.

| Family Dytiscidae |

7 a Antennae **short,** difficult to see, with wide flat segments (second segment greatly enlarged). Last segment of the tarsi not swollen at the tip.

second segment

Antenna

| Family Dryopidae |

b Antennae **longer and thread-like** (possibly slightly clubbed). Last segment of the tarsi large and swollen at the tip.

last tarsal segment

| Family Elminthidae |

8 a Head **extended** in front of eyes to form a snout. Antennae bent in the middle and clubbed at the tip.

| Family Curculionidae |
| Weevils |

b Head **without** such a snout. Antennae fairly long and thread-like.

| Family Chrysomelidae |

Some common or conspicuous water beetles

1   **Family Dytiscidae.** A family of powerful swimmers mostly inhabiting still
    water. The hind swimming legs, the thread-like eleven segmented antennae
    and the strong jaws are distinctive. The hind legs move in unison. A large
    family with over one hundred species.

The genus *Dytiscus*, which includes *Dytiscus marginalis*,
the Great Diving Beetle, can be recognised by the large
size of the species (22–34 mm long) and by the
colouration (pitchy to greenish-black with yellow sides
to the thorax and wing cases).

> *Dytiscus marginalis*

Acilius sulcatus, the Furrowed Beetle, is moderately large
(16–18 mm long) with distinctive black markings on the
head and thorax.

> *Acilius sulcatus*

Ilybius fuliginosus, the Mud Dweller, is a bronze beetle
with yellow margins to the wing-cases. It is rather
narrower than other dytiscids.

> *Ilybius fuliginosus*

Platambus maculatus is reddish-yellow with black
markings. It is found at the margins of running water.

> *Platambus maculatus*

Markings on
dorsal surface

Colymbetes fuscus is yellowish-green with fine black
markings across the wing-cases.

> *Colymbetes fuscus*

2 Family Gyrinidae (Whirligig beetles). Easily recognised in the field by their habit of rapidly whirling round on the surface of water and disappearing beneath it when disturbed. Only twelve British species.

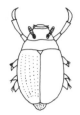

> *Gyrinus* species

3 Family Hydrophilidae. The aquatic members of this family are generally found in ponds and slow streams with ample vegetation. Many of the species are poor swimmers which spend most of their time crawling about on plants. The hind legs move alternately through the water; they do not beat in unison as in the Dytiscidae. A large family with over one hundred British species.

Hydrophilus piceus, the Great Silver Beetle, is easily recognised by its large size (3–4 cm long).

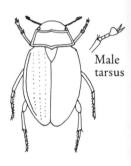

Male
tarsus

Hydrochara (Hydrophilus) caraboides is about 15 mm long and resembles the Great Silver Beetle in general form.

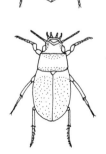

Other members of this family are less than 1 cm long.

4 Family Hygrobiidae. The only British species in this family is *Hygrobia hermanni*, the Screech Beetle. It is found in organically rich ponds and usually makes a squeaking sound when caught.

> *Hygrobia hermanni*

5 **Family Haliplidae**. The large ventral plates covering the bases of the hind legs are distinctive. Members of this family are found mainly in ponds and ditches but sometimes in running water. They are rather poor swimmers. Only eighteen British species.

 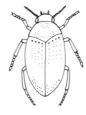

Ventral view   Dorsal view

6 **Family Dryopidae**. A family of small stream-dwelling beetles with hairy bodies. The antennae are distinctive. Only eight British species.

7 **Family Elminthidae**. A family of small stream-dwelling beetles found clinging to stones and logs. Only eleven British species.

8 **Family Curculionidae (Weevils)**. A large, mainly terrestrial family. Some species live on aquatic plants and may be found under water. The group is easily recognised by the shape of the head.

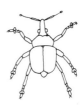

9 **Family Chrysomelidae**. A mainly terrestrial family but three genera (*Donacia*, *Plateumaris* and *Macroplea*) have larvae that obtain oxygen from the roots of aquatic plants.

A key to the families of freshwater fly larvae (order Diptera)

This key consists of three sections. Select which section to use by comparing your specimen with the information contained in the section headings. Then work through the descriptions in the section until one fitting your specimen is reached.

Section A   Midge and gnat larvae (Nematocera, excluding Tipulidae and Ptychopteridae)

Head capsule complete (i.e. sclerotised plates completely surround the head) and not retractable into the prothorax. Never more than two pairs of prolegs. (Midge and gnat larvae.)

1   Transparent larvae **with two pairs of air sacs**. Hang motionless in midwater. Up to 12 mm long.

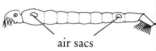

air sacs

Chaoborus species

> Family Chaoboridae
> Phantom midge larvae

2   Larvae with a swollen thorax and a pair of spiracles at the posterior end. Hang from the water surface or swim through the water. Anopheline mosquito larvae hang parallel to the water surface. They have no respiratory siphon. Culicine larvae hang down at an angle to the water surface. The spiracles open at the end of the respiratory siphon. Up to 12 mm long.

Anopheles species

Culex species

> Family Culicidae
> Mosquito larvae

3   U-shaped larvae. Thorax not swollen but with posterior spiracles. Hang from the water surface at the water's edge. Up to 12 mm long.

Dixa species

> Family Dixidae
> Dixid midge larvae

4 Dumb-bell-shaped larvae with a basal pad of very fine hooks, and a single proleg on the thorax. Found attached to solid objects in flowing water. Up to 8 mm long.

> Family Simuliidae
> Buffalo gnat or Black-fly larvae

Simulium species

5 Larvae with hairy plates on their backs (26 in *Pericoma*; fewer in *Psychoda*). In damp moss and rotting vegetation at the waters edge. Up to 6 mm long.

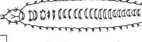

> Family Psychodidae
> Moth fly larvae

Pericoma species

6 Larvae with paired prolegs on the first and last body segments. Without lateral hairy projections. Bottom dwelling. Up to 15 mm long. The fisherman's 'blood worm' is the larval stage of the Harlequin Fly, *Chironomus*. Like some other chironomid larvae it is blood red but can be distinguished by the possession of two pairs of central tubuli.

paired prolegs

Chironomus species

tubuli

> Family Chironomidae
> Larvae of non-biting midges

7 **a** Resembling chironomid larvae above but with only posterior prolegs. Up to 4 mm long.

b Long thin snake-like larvae without prolegs. Up to 4 mm long.

c Larvae with lateral hairy projections. Up to 4 mm long.

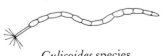

Culicoides species

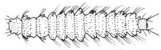

Atrichopogon species

> Family Ceratopogonidae
> Larvae of biting midges

Section B Brachycera, tipulid and ptychopterid larvae

Head capsule either incomplete (only partially sclerotised) or retractable into the prothorax. Several pairs of prolegs may be present.

1 Grub-like larvae with posterior spiracles surrounded by hairy processes. *Tipula* and *Dicranota* species are up to 15 mm long. *Pedicia* has the habit of inflating and deflating the penultimate segment. *Phalacrocera* larvae have long branched or shorter leaf-like processes on the dorsal surface. Up to 20 mm long.

Phalacrocera species

Tipula species

Dicranota species

> Family Tipulidae
> Crane fly larvae

2 Larvae with long telescopic breathing tube. Up to 7 cm long.

breathing tube

Ptychoptera species

> Family Ptychopteridae

3 Flattened body with slit-like breathing openings surrounded by hairs. Head not retractable. Up to 2 cm long.

Stratiomys species

> Family Stratiomyidae
> Soldier fly larvae

4 Larvae with tapering front and hind ends; thickened rings between segments each with eight prolegs. Up to 15 mm long.

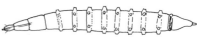

Tabanus species

> Family Tabanidae
> Horse fly or Cleg larvae

Section C Cyclorrhapha larvae

Larvae without a head capsule. Mouthparts reduced and permanently retracted into the prothorax.

1 Larvae with spiracles close together at the end of a long single telescopic breathing tube. Up to 15 mm long.

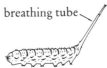

breathing tube

> Family Syrphidae
> Drone fly larvae

Tubifera species

2 Larvae with posterior spiracles at the ends of two retractable tubes (or two sharp hollow spines which can be inserted into plant tissue). Up to 10 mm long.

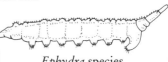

> Family Ephydridae
> Shore fly larvae

Ephydra species

3 Larvae with posterior spiracles not on tubes or hollow spines. Up to 8 mm long.

> Family Muscidae

Limnophora species

Larvae of other Cyclorrhapha families may also be found in freshwater.

Spiders and mites (phylum Chelicerata)

Only one species of spider (the Water Spider, *Argyroneta aquatica*) actually lives in water. However the Raft Spider, *Dolomedes fimbriatus*, can move below the water surface when disturbed. Other species are often knocked into the water when sampling. There are over three hundred species of British water mite (Acarina). Most are brightly coloured and small (1–8 mm). Unlike spiders, mites have a body that is not divided into two parts.

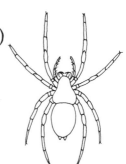

Argyroneta aquatica

Examples of mites

Freshwater crustaceans (phylum Crustacea)

1 **a** Crustaceans **with a flat shield-like carapace, two suckers** and **four pairs of swimming limbs.** Parasitic on fish but often found swimming in open water.

sucker
swimming limbs

> *Argulus foliaceus*
> Fish-louse

   b Crustaceans **without this combination of features. No suckers.** ──▶ 2

2 **a** **Small** crustaceans usually less than 5 mm long. If longer, they are transparent and found swimming in open water. ──────────▶ 3

   b **Large- or medium-sized** crustaceans usually more than 5 mm long. Found crawling or swimming near the bottom. ──────────▶ 5

3 **a** Whole body **including head** enclosed by a carapace with two valves, hinged dorsally and open ventrally (rather like a mussel shell). Often resembling a plant seed. About eighty British species.

carapace

> Ostracoda

Cypris species

   b If a bivalved carapace is present, it **does not enclose the head.** ──────▶ 4

4 **a** Body obviously **segmented** and without a carapace. Usually somewhat pear-shaped. Second antennae small and never used for locomotion. About one hundred British species.

> Copepoda

   b Body, but not the head, generally enclosed in a bivalved carapace. Usually **no trace of segmentation** except for limbs. Second antennae large, branched and used for locomotion. About ninety British species.

> Cladocera

Daphnia species

Bosmina species

Polyphemus species

Leptodora species

5 a Crustaceans **with a carapace** covering the thorax. Eyes on stalks. Body resembling a small lobster with large pincers.

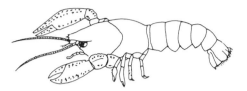

> Order Decapoda
> *Austropotamobius pallipes*
> Crayfish

b Crustaceans **without a carapace** (therefore the segments of the thorax are visible from above). Eyes not on stalks. ──────────────▶ 6

6 a Body **flattened dorsoventrally**. Resembles a Woodlouse or Slater.

> Order Isopoda
> *Asellus* species
> Freshwater hog-louse

b Body **flattened from side to side.** Resembles a Sandhopper.

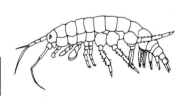

> Order Amphipoda
> Freshwater 'shrimps'

──────────────▶ 7

7 a Dorsal surface of last three abdominal segments **with tufts of spines and setae.** Frequently progresses on its side.

> *Gammarus* species

b Dorsal surface of the last three abdominal segments **without spines or setae.** Crawls about upright.

> *Crangonyx pseudogracilis*

Freshwater mussels
(phylum Mollusca; class Bivalvia)

1 **a** **Medium-sized** mussels (usually 4–5 cm long) with alternating wavy bands of brown and yellow. Attached to substratum by threads.

> *Dreissena polymorpha*
> Zebra mussel

b **Small** or **large** mussels (usually less than 2 cm or more than 5 cm long) without such bands. ──────────────▶ 2

2 **a** Small rather globular mussels, under 3 cm long.

──────────────▶ 3

b Large ovate or elliptical mussels, at least 4 cm long.

──────────────▶ 4

3 **a** With **two siphons**. Shell more or less symmetrical about a hinge, usually more than 1 cm long.

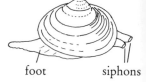

> *Sphaerium* species
> Orb-shells

foot   siphons

b With **only one siphon**. Shell less symmetrical, usually less than 1 cm long.

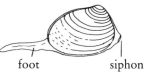

> *Pisidium* species
> Pea mussels

foot   siphon

a Shell **with a depression in front of the umbo**. Hinge with teeth.

Unio species (also the Pearl mussel *Margaritifera*)	

umbo   depression

b Shell **without such a depression**. Hinge without teeth.

Anodonta species Swan mussels and Duck mussels	

umbo

Common British freshwater snails and limpets (phylum Mollusca; class Gastropoda)

This key is based mainly on shell features which can be seen in either living or preserved material. Estuarine and semi-aquatic species are not included. Shell measurements should be determined carefully using callipers or a micrometer screw gauge.

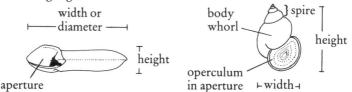

1 **a** Shell limpet-like, conical with **no trace of coiling**.

Family Ancylidae Freshwater limpets

▶ 2

   b Shell snail-like, **spirally wound or coiled**.

▶ 3

2 **a** Shell **a low narrow cone**; height less than half the length, breadth about half the length. Found on plants in lakes and rivers. Width of 5 mm.

Acroloxus lacustris The lake limpet

   b Shell **taller and wider**; height more than half the length, breadth greater than half the length. Found on rocks and stones in lakes and rivers. Width of 8 mm.

Ancylus fluviatilis The river limpet

3 **a** Snails **with an operculum** (a plate carried on the back of the snail which closes the aperture of the shell when the animal is withdrawn).

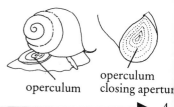

operculum   operculum closing apertur

▶ 4

   b Snails **without an operculum**. ──────────▶ 9

4   **a** Shell over 30 mm high, usually **banded**.

> | Family Viviparidae | ———————▶ 5

    b Shell less than 15 mm high, may be patterned but seldom banded. ——▶ 6

5   **a** Shell **broad** and **glossy** with a large conspicuous umbilicus. Height of 36 mm.

> | *Viviparus fasciatus*
> | Lister's river snail

umbilicus

    b Shell **narrower** and **not glossy** with the umbilicus hardly apparent. Height of 34 mm.

> | *Viviparus viviparus*
> | The river snail

6   **a** Shell thick and robust with a **low spire** and a **D-shaped aperture**; usually variegated purple, pink or white on a yellow or brown background. Height of 7 mm. Width of 9 mm.

> | Family Neritidae
> | *Theodoxus fluviatilis*
> | The nerite

    b Shell **not of this form**, not variegated. ——————————▶ 7

7   **a** Shell **wider than tall** or width and height about equal.

> | Family Valvatidae

Valvata cristata

Valvata macrostoma

Valvata piscinalis

    b Shell much **taller than wide**.

> | Family Hydrobiidae | ———————▶ 8

8 a Shell at least 6 mm high and 4 mm broad. Operculum **with concentric lines, not retractable** beyond the aperture of the shell.

closed umbilicus   open umbilicus

Bithynia tentaculata   *Bithynia lea*

Bithynia species

b Shell under 6 mm high and 4 mm broad. Operculum **with a spiral line, retractable** beyond the aperture of the shell. Very common, especially in flowing water. Height of 5 mm.

closed umbilicus

Potamopyrgus jenkinsi
Jenkin's spire shell

9 a Shell **flat, much broader than tall,** coiled almost in one plane with spire not projecting above the last whorl.

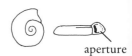

aperture

Family Planorbidae
Ramshorn snails

There are at least fourteen species of British ramshorn snails in four different genera. The Great Ramshorn (*Planorbarius corneus*) can easily be recognised by its large size (over 20 mm in diameter and up to 12 mm high).

b Shell **a conical spiral** with spire usually projecting above the last whorl.

10

10   **a** Shell **sinistral**, i.e. if it is held with the spire pointing upwards and the aperture facing you the aperture is on your left.

aperture

> ### Family Physidae

————————————————————————▶ 11

  b Shell **dextral**, i.e. if held as above the aperture is on your right.

aperture

> ### Family Lymnaeidae

————————————————————————▶ 12

11   **a** Shell **elongate** and **pointed**; aperture height of just over half the height of the shell. Height of 10 mm.

aperture height

> ### *Aplexa hypnorum*
> ### The moss bladder snail

  b Shell **more globose**; aperture height of about three-quarters of the shell height. Height of 11 mm.

> ### *Physa fontinalis*
> ### The bladder snail

12   **a** Shell with a **tall spire**; aperture height of less than two-thirds of the shell height. ————————————————————▶ 13

  b Shell with a **short spire**; aperture height of more than two-thirds of the shell height. ——————————————————▶ 16

13 a Large species, height of 35–50 mm; spire **acutely pointed**; last whorl very large.

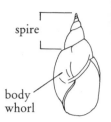

spire

body whorl

> *Lymnaea stagnalis*
> The great pond snail

b Smaller species, height up to 25 mm; spire **less acutely pointed**; last whorl not so large. ──────────────────▶ 14

14 a Aperture **small**, about one-third of the shell height. Height of 11 mm.

> *Lymnaea glabra*
> The mud snail

b Aperture **larger**, about one-half of the shell height. ──────────▶ 15

15 a Shell height of 19–24 mm; umbilicus **closed by aperture lip**; shell with longitudinal and spiral sculpturing.

closed umbilicus

> *Lymnaea palustris*
> The marsh snail

b Shell height of 8–12 mm; ubilicus **open**; shell with fine longitudinal striations.

open umbilicus

> *Lymnaea truncatula*
> The dwarf pond snail

16 **a** Shell **thin** and **transparent** with a very low blunt spire (when the animal is extended, the body almost covers the shell). Height of 16 mm.

> *Myxas glutinosa*
> The glutinous snail

b Shell **thicker and not transparent**; spire longer and somewhat pointed (the body is not extended over the shell when expanded). ──────▶ 17

17 **a** Last whorl expanded into a large **ear-shaped aperture**; spire **short** but **sharply pointed** (in life the shell is carried with the spire pointing **sideways**). Height of 21 mm.

> *Lymnaea auricularia*
> The ear pond snail

b Shell **variable** but the last whorl is usually less expanded; spire **less sharply pointed** (in life the shell is carried with the spire pointing **backwards**).

> *Lymnaea peregra*
> The wandering snail

A key to the more common British freshwater leeches (phylum Annelida; class Hirudinea)

Sixteen species of leech are known to occur in Britain but only the eleven most familiar species are included here. The key should be used to identify living leeches but it may be necessary to anaesthetise active specimens lightly with soda water in order to observe the number and arrangement of eyes. These may be seen more clearly if the head is gently compressed (not squashed!) between glass slides. Care should be taken to examine the sides of the head as well as the top. Leeches are segmented animals (with about thirty-four segments) but the segments are subdivided externally into a number of rings (annuli) which are more easy to discern than the true segments.

1 a Leeches **with two to six eyes** all of which are found on top of the head. ——————————————————————————————————▶ **2**

b Leeches **with eight or ten eyes**, some of which may be situated on the sides of the head. ——————————————————————————————▶ **6**

2 a Body at rest **cylindrical**, about ten times as long as wide, with over two hundred annuli. Both anterior and posterior suckers distinct from the body.

anterior sucker   posterior sucker

> Family Piscicolidae
> *Piscicola geometra*
> The fish leech

b Body at rest **flattened**, less than ten times as long as wide, with fewer than eighty annuli. Anterior sucker less distinct from the body.

Family Glossiphoniidae, in part ——————————————————▶ **3**

3 a Body **with a small callous scute** about one-sixth of the way along its dorsal surface. Only one pair of eyes. Creamy white or transparent leeches flecked with grey, green or brown.

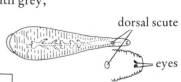

dorsal scute

eyes

> *Helobdella stagnalis*

b Body **without a dorsal scute**. Usually with more than one pair of eyes. ——————————————————————————————————▶ **4**

4 **a** Head at rest broader than the body segments just behind it. Usually with **two pairs of eyes** but the first pair may be reduced or absent. Green or yellow–brown leeches usually with seven rows of yellow spots.

Head

| *Hemiclepsis marginata* |

b Head at rest is not broader than the body segments just behind it. Typically with **three pairs of eyes** but these may be fused in various ways giving the impression of fewer eyes.

| *Glossiphonia* species | ——————————▶ 5

5 **a** Translucent **amber-coloured** leeches **without prominent papillae** (minute conical protuberances) on the dorsal surface. Adults at rest are less than 15 mm long. Typically the first pair of eyes are closer together than the other two pairs.

| *Glossiphonia heteroclita* |

b Leeches marked with **green and brown** with **prominent papillae** present on the dorsal surface of every third annulus. Adults at rest are more than 15 mm long. Eyes normally in two parallel rows.

| *Glossiphonia complanata* |

6 **a** Large leeches with **ten eyes** arranged in the form of a crescent. Adults at rest are 6 cm or more in length. Mouth armed with toothed jaws (difficult to see without slitting open the head).

| Family Hirudinidae | ——————————▶ 10

b Leeches with only **eight eyes**. Usually adults at rest are less than 4 cm in length but *Trocheta* can grow up to 10 cm. Jawless. ——————————▶ 7

7 a Eyes **in two longitudinal rows** on top of the head. Mouth very small with a pore on the anterior sucker. Olive-grey, amber or greenish leeches with a soft rather gelatinous body.

> Family Glossiphoniidae, in part
> *Theromyzon tessulatum*

b Eyes **in two transverse rows** extending onto sides of the head. Mouth large, occupying the entire cavity of the anterior sucker.

> Family Erpobdellidae ────────────▶ 8

8 a Large greyish-green or reddish leeches sometimes with two longitudinal brown lines. Adults at rest are up to 10 cm long. Body flattened **posteriorly** but more cylindrical anteriorly. Typically, groups of broad annuli alternate with groups of narrow annuli.

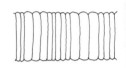

> *Trocheta subviridis*

b Smaller leeches. Adults at rest are less than 4 cm long. Body flattened **along its whole length**. All annuli of approximately the same width.

> *Erpobdella* species
> Worm leeches ──────────▶ 9

9 a Reddish-brown leeches **without any black pigment** on the dorsal surface; **no yellow pigment** deeper in body.

> *Erpobdella testacea*

b Dorsal surface marked **with at least flecks of black pigment; yellow pigment visible** deeper in body.

> *Erpobdella octoculata*

10 a Dorsal surface of body with obvious **reddish-yellow longitudinal stripes**. Anus **scarcely visible**. Jaws capable of piercing human skin.

> *Hirudo medicinalis*
> The medicinal leech

b Dorsal surface of body with **broken khaki–brown stripes** or **without stripes**. Anus **distinct**. Jaws incapable of piercing human skin.

posterior sucker

anus

> *Haemopis sanguisuga*
> The horse leech

British freshwater flatworms (phylum Platyhelminthes)

Free-living flatworms (class Turbellaria) are represented by two orders in British freshwaters:

Order Rhabdocoelida Small flatworms, mostly under 2 mm long, in which the gut is a simple tube opening near the front of the body (there are probably about two hundred species in Britain).

Order Tricladida Larger flatworms, usually more than 6 mm long, in which the gut has three branches, one leading forwards and two backwards from the proboscis located ventrally in the middle of the body (there are eleven freshwater species in Britain).
(The identification of rhabdocoels is beyond the scope of this work.)

A key to the British species of freshwater triclads

N.B. This key is based on features which can be seen in living specimens. Preserved worms are almost impossible to identify unless special precautions are taken.

1 a Triclads **with numerous eye-spots** along the front and side margins of the head.

———————————————————————▶ 2

 b Triclads **with only two (sometimes four) eyes** located away from the margins of the head.

———————————————————————▶ 3

2 a Head **with awl-shaped tentacles**. Ventral surface of the animal paler than the dorsal surface. The colour is brown to brownish-black.

> *Polycelis felina*

 b Head **without such tentacles**. Ventral surface of the animal is the same colour as the dorsal surface.

> *Polycelis nigra* and
> *Polycelis tenuis*

Although *Polycelis nigra* is commonly black with the pigmentation uniformly distributed and *Polycelis tenuis* is usually light or dark brown with a rather mottled appearance, colour is not a reliable character for the separation of these two species. Certain identification requires the examination of the penis in squash preparations.

3 **a** Head with **awl-shaped tentacles** on the anterio-lateral corners of the head. The colour is grey to black, and sometimes brown, with a paler ventral surface.

> *Crenobia alpina*

b Head **without awl-shaped tentacles** in this position. ——————▶ 4

4 **a** Head much narrower than the trunk and **with a distinct 'neck'**. A distinct 'sucker' present between the eyes. The colour is brownish, often with darker spots or blotches.

'sucker'

'neck'

> *Bdellocephala punctata*

b Head **not of this form**. No sucker. ——————▶ 5

5 **a** Eyes **close together** (the distance between them is less than the distance from the eyes to the anterior margin of the head).

——————▶ 6

b Eyes **farther apart** (the distance between them is greater than the distance from the eyes to the anterior margin of the head).

——————▶ 8

6 **a** Head **triangular** with pronounced lateral projections. The colour is mottled grey–brown with a paler ventral surface.

lateral projection

> *Dugesia tigrina*

b Head **truncate** without any trace of tentacles or projections. ——————▶ 7

7   a Pigmented, brown or grey–black triclads.

> *Planaria torva*

b Unpigmented, white triclads.

> *Phagocata vitta*

8   a Head **truncate** (widest at the front) with slight anterio-lateral projections. Unpigmented, white triclads (the food in the gut may give some variable colouration).

> *Dendrocoelum lacteum*

b Head **spatulate** or **bluntly triangular** (widest a little behind the front). Pigmented, brown, black or grey. ─────────────▶   9

9   a Anterior border of head **bluntly pointed** when crawling. Body squat and neck indistinct. The colour is usually uniformly black or brown with a ventral surface of the same colour.

> *Dugesia lugubris*

b Anterior border of head **rounded** when crawling. Body slender and neck more distinct. The colour is usually brown or mottled grey with a paler ventral surface.

> *Dugesia polychroa*

Aquatic worms

Section A   Segmented worms (Oligochaeta)

Many species of segmented worms are found in water, ranging from small transparent worms, less than 1 mm long, up to larger animals resembling garden earthworms. It is impossible, however, to identify most species without making microscopical preparations to examine the setae (bristles) which are arranged in four bundles on each segment.

Oligochaetes with more than two setae in each bundle

1   **Family Naididae.** Small transparent worms usually less than 2 cm long. Sometimes a chain of asexually produced individuals is found. Some species with eyes.

Nais species   *Stylaria* species

2   **Family Tubificidae.** Larger reddish worms that coil tightly when disturbed. Never with eyes.

3   **Family Enchytraeidae (Potworms).** Usually whitish worms, up to about 3 cm long. No eyes. Mainly terrestrial.

Oligochaetes with only two setae in each bundle

4   **Family Lumbriculidae.** *Stylodrilus* resembles a tubificid. Mature individuals have non-retractable penes on the tenth segment.

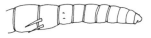

Stylodrilus species

Lumbriculus is red–brown in colour with a distinctly greenish anterior end.

5   **Family Lumbricidae.** *Eiseniella tetraedra* resembles an earthworm but the posterior end is square in cross-section.

Section B   Roundworms, etc. (Nematoda and allies)

Roundworms are very common animals at the bottom of streams and ponds but most of the species are small and easily overlooked.

1   **Rainworms (Merminthidae).** Nematodes which range in length from 1 mm to 50 cm. For part of their lives they are parasites, living inside insects or other animals, but the adults may be found in soil or mud. (Species found in soil often appear after rain, and hence the name.)

2   **Horsehair worms (Nematomorpha).** Long worms which look like thick horsehairs. The life history is similar to that of rainworms, the young worms living inside insects and other animals. Whereas a rainworm has a pointed front end, the front end of a horsehair worm is blunt. Horsehair worms are not nematodes.

Bibliography

The following list contains those works most likely to be used by students. For more detailed lists, see Armitage, Furse and Wright (1979) and Maitland (1977).

Armitage, P.D., Furse, M.T. and Wright, J.F. (1979). *A Bibliography of Works for the Identification of Freshwater Invertebrates in the British Isles.* Occasional Publications of the Freshwater Biological Association No. 5.
Macan, T.T. (1959). *A Guide to Freshwater Invertebrate Animals.* Longman.
Maitland, P.S. (1977). *A Coded Checklist of Animals occurring in Fresh Water in the British Isles.* Institute of Terrestrial Ecology, Edinburgh.
Quigley, M. (1977). *Invertebrates of Streams and Rivers: a key to identification.* Edward Arnold, London.

Plecoptera
Hynes, H.B.N. (1977). *A Key to the Adults and Nymphs of the British Stoneflies (Plecoptera)* (3rd edn.). Scientific Publications of the Freshwater Biological Association No. 17.

Ephemeroptera
Macan, T.T. (1979). *A Key to the Nymphs of the British Species of Ephemeroptera with Notes on their Ecology.* (3rd edn.). Scientific Publications of the Freshwater Biological Association No. 20.

Odonata
Hammond, C.O. (1977). *The Dragonflies of Great Britain and Ireland.* Curwen, London.

Hemiptera
Macan, T.T. (1965). *A Revised Key to the British Water Bugs (Hemiptera–Heteroptera).* (2nd edn.). Scientific Publications of the Freshwater Biological Association No. 16.

Coleoptera
Balfour-Browne, F. (1940). *British Water Beetles,* Vol. 1. Ray Society, London.
Balfour-Browne, F. (1950). *British Water Beetles,* Vol. 2. Ray Society, London.
Balfour-Browne, F. (1958). *British Water Beetles,* Vol. 3. Ray Society, London.
Joy, N.H. (1932). *A Practical Handbook of British Beetles,* Vol. 1. (text), Vol. 2 (figures). Witherby, London.

Trichoptera
Edington, J.M. and Hildrew, A.G. (1981). *Caseless Caddis Larvae of the British Isles.* Scientific Publications of the Freshwater Biological Association No. 43.
Hickin, N.E. (1967). *Caddis Larvae; Larvae of the British Trichoptera.* Hutchinson, London.

Diptera
Cranston, P.S. (1982). *A Key to the Larvae of the British Orthocladiinae (Chironomidae).* Scientific Publications of the Freshwater Biological Association No. 45.

Davies, L. (1968). *A Key to the British Species of Simuliidae (Diptera) in the Larval, Pupal, and Adult Stages.* Scientific Publications of the Freshwater Biological Association No. 24.

Disney, R.H.L. (1975). *A Key to the Larvae, Pupae and Adults of the British Dixidae (Diptera), the Meniscus Midges.* Scientific Publications of the Freshwater Biological Association No. 31.

Mattingly, P.F. (1950). Diptera: Nematocera (part). Family Culicidae: Subfamily Culicinae. *Handbook of the Identification of British Insects,* 9 (2) 102–120.

Other aquatic insects

Elliott, J.M. (1977). *A Key to the Larvae and Adults of British Freshwater Megaloptera and Neuroptera.* Scientific Publications of the Freshwater Biological Association No. 35.

Crustaceans

Gledhill, T., Sutcliffe, D.W. and Williams, W.D. (1976). *A Revised Key to the British Species of Crustacea: Malacostraca Occurring in Fresh Water.* Scientific Publications of the Freshwater Biological Association No. 31.

Harding, J.P. and Smith, W.A. (1974). *A Key to the British Freshwater Cyclopoid and Calanoid Copepods* (2nd edn.) Scientific Publications of the Freshwater Biological Association No. 18.

Scourfield, D.J. and Harding, J.P. (1966). *A Key to the British Species of Freshwater Cladocera with Notes on their Ecology* (3rd edn.) Scientific Publications of the Freshwater Biological Association No. 5.

Mollusca

Ellis, A.E. (1978). *British Freshwater Bivalve Mollusca.* Synopnis British Fauna (New Series) No. 11. Linnean Society.

Macan, T.T. (1977). *A Key to the British Fresh- and Brackish-water Gastropods with Notes on their Ecology* (4th edn.). Scientific Publications of the Freshwater Biological Association No. 13.

Hirudinea

Elliott, J.M.C. (1979). *A Key to the British Freshwater Leeches.* Scientific Publications of the Freshwater Biological Association No. 40.

Tricladida

Reynoldson, T.B. (1978). *A Key to the British Species of Freshwater Triclads* (2nd edn.). Scientific Publications of the Freshwater Biological Association No. 23.

Oligochaeta

Brinkhurst, R.O. (1971). *A Guide for the Identification of British Aquatic Oligochaeta* (2nd edn.). Scientific Publications of the Freshwater Biological Association No. 22.